Contents

GW00866108

Name: _____

1 All about me!

Tell your friends something about yourself. Begin by writing some sentences. Then use connectives to join your sentences together in one paragraph.

Think about this!

Since you began your last Handwriting folder, you have grown quite a bit. Think about how you have changed and what you have learned during the past year. At the end of this year, you will be able to look back to see how you have progressed.

Design a cover for your handwriting folder

Set out a title for your handwriting folder. Add your name, class and the date to the front cover. Then you might decorate the borders with patterns.

My _____
Handwriting folder

Name _____

Class _____

Date _____

Here are some patterns that you might use to decorate your work.
Try these first and then design some patterns of your own.

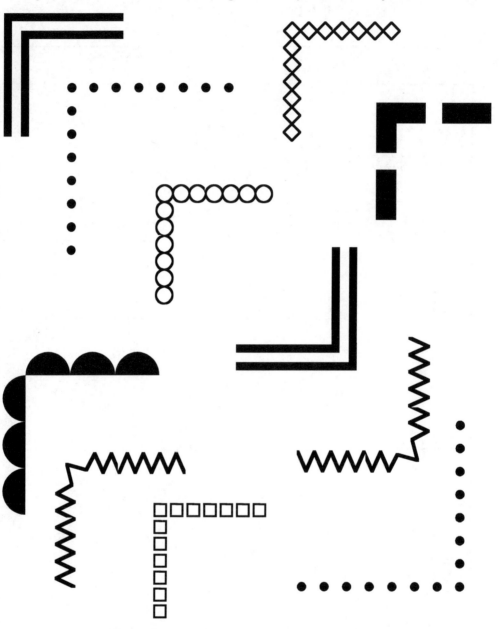

Think about this!

Repeating a pattern is a very simple way to decorate things.
You might make your own bookmark or decorate your
schoolbooks or homework files, but first ask your teacher
for permission!
A copied poem looks very attractive with a decorated border.

Letter joins

ar ai ab un

Write as many words as you can think of that contain one
or more of these letter joins.

ar

_____

_____

_____

_____

ai

_____

_____

_____

_____

ab

_____

_____

_____

_____

un

_____

_____

_____

_____

5 Letter joins

ou ri wi it

Write as many words as you can think of that contain one
or more of these letter joins.

ou

_____

_____

_____

_____

ri

_____

_____

_____

_____

wi

_____

_____

_____

_____

it

_____

_____

_____

_____

Letter joins

al   ul   ot   wh

Write as many words as you can think of that contain one
or more of these letter joins.

(*al*) _____

_____

_____

_____

(*ul*) _____

_____

_____

_____

(*ot*) _____

_____

_____

_____

(*wh*) _____

_____

_____

_____

7　A verse for a Valentine card

Write this well-known verse. Then you may like to write
a version of your own.

Roses are red,
Violets are blue,
Sugar is sweet
And so are You!

_____

_____

_____

_____

_____

_____

Think about this!

People like to send and receive Valentine cards.
The cards should be anonymous, so people have
to guess who they are from.
Sometimes, the verses are funny and even cheeky.
Make a Valentine card for someone you like.

8 Design a card

Design a card to celebrate a special occasion. Choose one of the occasions listed below or one of your own. Decorate the borders.

Happy Birthday!   Congratulations!
Happy Anniversary   Merry Christmas
Happy New Year   Good Luck!

9 Address an envelope

Now set out the address of the person you will send your card to.
You might use the address of one of your friends or make one up.

Think about this!

Remember to use the correct punctuation in the address.
Be especially careful with abbreviations.
Don't forget the postcode!

10 A postcard to a friend

Turn this page on its side and write a postcard to a friend describing a holiday.
Don't forget to mention the weather!

To:

Here are some terms you might hear during a weather forecast.
Copy them out in your best handwriting.

> a bracing breeze   occasional showers
> good clear spells   heavy cloud cover
> dry and sunny   a slight flurry of snow
> long periods of sunshine
> dense mist over high ground   a sharp frost
> some danger of flooding   blizzard conditions

12 Some words you should know

Write the words in the box in alphabetical order. Then practise reading and spelling them with your partner.

Think about this!

To help you remember these words, practise writing each one at least five times.
Remember to Look, Say, Cover, Write and Check!
Try not to lift your pencil off the paper until you have finished a whole word.
When you have finished, place your pencil on the line and try writing each word again with your eyes closed.

coming can't asked do not doesn't
began don't did not cannot didn't
does not brought

13 Apostrophes

Each of the words and phrases in the box can be shortened by using an apostrophe. Write the shortened version of each as many times as you can on one line, making sure you put the apostrophe in the correct place.

Think about this!

If you remember that the apostrophe replaces the missing letter or letters, it should help you to put it in the correct place. If you forget, look back to activity 12.

> I am   he will   it is   she has   I will   will not
> do not   shall not   did not   would not

_____

_____

_____

_____

_____

_____

_____

_____

_____

_____

_____

_____

_____

Some words you should know

Write the words in the box in alphabetical order. Then practise reading and spelling them with your partner.

Think about this!

To help you remember these words, practise writing each one at least five times.
Remember to Look, Say, Cover, Write and Check!
Try not to lift your pencil off the paper until you have finished a whole word.
When you have finished, place your pencil on the line and try writing each word again with your eyes closed.

> stopped I'm gone opened heard started
> leave know show I am jumped knew

Write the words in the box in alphabetical order. Then practise reading and spelling them with your partner.

Think about this!

To help you remember these words, practise writing each one at least five times.
Remember to Look, Say, Cover, Write and Check!
Try not to lift your pencil off the paper until you have finished a whole word.
When you have finished, place your pencil on the line and try writing each word again with your eyes closed.

tries woken think watch turned used
write woke thought walked told

_____

_____

_____

_____

_____

_____

_____

_____

_____

_____

_____

_____

16 Compound words

Make ten compound words by joining a word from the first box
with a word from the second box.

Think about this!

Compound words are made up of shorter words.
Each of the compound words on this page has two parts,
e.g. walk + about = walkabout.
You might make some matching cards for younger
children, writing each part of a compound word on
one side of a jigsaw piece and illustrating it on the other.

snow play round bath corn sun moon
star rain sea

ground fish about man light flake coat
flower room side

_____

_____

_____

_____

_____

_____

_____

_____

17 Compound words

Add the prefix "al" to each of the words in the box, then write each
new compound word as many times as you can on one line.
Can you think of any more compound words featuring the "al" prefix?

Think about this! Each of the new compound words has two parts.
Draw a line between the syllables in each word.
You might make some matching cards for younger
children, writing each part of a compound word on one
side of a jigsaw piece and illustrating it on the other.

> most though ready so arm together cove
> low right ways as tar arming

_____

_____

_____

_____

_____

_____

_____

_____

_____

Compound words

Make eight compound words by joining a word from
the first box with a word from the second box and a word
from the third box.

Think about this!

Compound words are made up of shorter words.
Each of the compound words on this page has
three parts, e.g. games + man + ship = gamesmanship.
You might make some matching cards for younger
children, writing each part of a compound word on one
side of a jigsaw piece.

in up here what in who here whom

to in side so so so side so

ever fore ever far ever after down out

_____

_____

_____

_____

_____

_____

_____

_____

Compound words

Use the words in the box to help you make as many two-part compound words as you can. Each word from the box can be used as the first part or the second part of different compound words. Write each new word as many times as you can on one line.

Think about this!

Underline the vowels and draw a line between the syllables in each of your new compound words. You might make some matching cards for younger children, writing each part of a compound word on one side of a jigsaw piece and illustrating it on the other.

after day rain night in out storm down snow under suit sea green

_____

_____

_____

_____

_____

_____

_____

_____

_____

_____

Here is the beginning of a story you may know. Write it in your best handwriting. You may want to draw your own picture of the Iron Man.

Think about this!

Ted Hughes was a famous poet who also wrote stories for children. He set out his writing almost like a poem. As you write, think about the punctuation. How do the commas help you to read the story aloud?

The Iron Man came to the top of the cliff.
How far had he walked? Nobody knows.
How was he made? Nobody knows.
Taller than a house, the Iron Man stood
at the top of the cliff, on the very brink,
in the darkness.
The wind sang through his iron fingers.
His great iron head, shaped like a dustbin
but as big as a bedroom, slowly turned to the
right, slowly turned to the left.
His iron ears turned, this way, that way.
He was hearing the sea.
His eyes, like headlamps, glowed white, then
red, then infra-red, searching the sea.
Never before had the Iron Man seen the sea.

Ted Hughes

Syllables

Write the two-syllable words in the box in alphabetical order. Underline all of the vowels in each word, then add a line to show where each syllable break is.

Think about this! You might make a set of syllable jigsaws for younger children, as you did with the compound words in activities 16–19.

> patter   flipper   shopper   hummer   finger
> dragon   thunder   monkey   flower   shadow
> cover   lightning   tiger

---

22 Syllables

Write the three-syllable words in the box in alphabetical order.
Underline all of the vowels in each word, then add a line to show
where each syllable break is.

Think about this! You might make a set of syllable jigsaws for younger children, as you did with the compound words in activities 16–19.

telephone butterfly supervise irrigate bicycle mystify holiday educate skeleton opening calendar motorway accident

23 Syllables

Write the multi-syllable words in the box in alphabetical order.
Underline all of the vowels in each word, then add a line to show
where each syllable break is.

Think about this!

You might make a set of syllable jigsaws for younger
children, as you did with the compound words in
activities 16–19.

meteorology hippopotamus explanation
rhinoceros onomatopoeia vaccination
astronomy environment tonsillectomy
terrestrial binoculars artificial identification

Handwriting check 2:
"The Intruder"

A kenning describes something without using its name. Think about which creatures are described by kennings in this poem. Write this poem in your best handwriting. You might decorate it with illustrations of all the creatures mentioned.

Think about this!

Look carefully at each line to see which has a comma and which a full stop.
Who do you think "Two-boots" is?

Two-boots in the forest walks,
Pushing through the bracken stalks.

Vanishing like a puff of smoke,
Nimbletail flies up the oak.

Long ears helter-skelter shoots
Into his house among the roots.

At work upon the highest bark,
Tapperbill knocks off to hark.

Painted-wings through sun and shade
Flounces off along the glade.

Not a creature lingers by,
When clumping Two-boots comes to pry.

James Reeves

"ph" says "f"

In Greek, an "f" sound is often made by using "ph". Write the words in the box in alphabetical order, then practise reading them aloud with your partner.

> *physical phew pharmacist photocopy pheasant phase phoneme phrase phonecard phantom photograph phobia physics*

_____

_____

_____

_____

_____

_____

_____

_____

_____

_____

_____

_____

26 "Please" sentences

Write each of the following sentences in your best handwriting.

Please do not walk on the grass.

_____

_____

_____

Please keep your dog on a lead.

_____

_____

_____

Please take your litter home with you.

_____

_____

_____

Please drive carefully.

_____

_____

_____

Write each of the following sentences in your best handwriting.

Thank you for coming.

Thank you for inviting me.

Thank you for not smoking.

Thank you for keeping our playground tidy.

"Do" and "Don't" sentences

Write each of the following sentences in your best handwriting.

Do keep your coats tidy.

Do remember to say "Please" and "Thank you".

Don't run in the corridors.

Don't fight in the playground.

Handwriting check 3:
Proverbs

Write each of the following proverbs in your best handwriting.

A stitch in time saves nine.

_____

_____

_____

Too many cooks spoil the broth.

_____

_____

_____

A fool and his money are soon parted.

_____

_____

_____

A watched pot never boils.

_____

_____

_____

Some words you should know

Write the words in the box in alphabetical order. Then practise reading and spelling them with your partner.

Think about this!

To help you remember these words, practise writing each one at least five times.
Remember to Look, Say, Cover, Write and Check!
Try not to lift your pencil off the paper until you have finished a whole word.
When you have finished, place your pencil on the line and try writing each word again with your eyes closed.

half   morning   during   almost   first   better
much   every   always   before   any

31 Some words you should know

Write the words in the box in alphabetical order. Then practise reading and spelling them with your partner.

Think about this!

To help you remember these words, practise writing each one at least five times.

Remember to Look, Say, Cover, Write and Check!

Try not to lift your pencil off the paper until you have finished a whole word.

When you have finished, place your pencil on the line and try writing each word again with your eyes closed.

only font number colon second hyphen
never connective often clause comma

_____

_____

_____

_____

_____

_____

_____

_____

_____

_____

_____

_____

Some words you should know

Write the words in the box in alphabetical order. Then practise reading and spelling them with your partner.

Think about this!

To help you remember these words, practise writing each one at least five times.
Remember to Look, Say, Cover, Write and Check!
Try not to lift your pencil off the paper until you have finished a whole word.
When you have finished, place your pencil on the line and try writing each word again with your eyes closed.

young today suddenly until sometimes year whole upon still those while

Write each of the following sentences in your best handwriting.

Think before you speak.

_____

_____

_____

Don't interrupt another speaker.

_____

_____

_____

Speak slowly and clearly.

_____

_____

_____

Listen carefully to the opinions of others.

_____

_____

_____

Single into plural

"*f*" into "*ves*"

Write the words in the box in their plural form.
Remember to change each word ending.

scarf life dwarf wife knife self leaf
loaf wolf calf elf sheaf hoof

_____

_____

_____

_____

_____

_____

_____

_____

_____

_____

_____

_____

Handwriting check 4:
Proverbs

Write each of the following proverbs in your best handwriting.

Red sky at night, shepherd's delight; red sky in the morning, shepherd's warning.

_____

_____

_____

_____

_____

_____

One swallow does not make a summer.

_____

_____

_____

Ne'er cast a clout till May be out.

_____

_____

_____

_____

Decorating letters

These capital letters illustrate different styles and decoration.
Draw each letter in a box in a different style and decorate them all.

B T D M S

Decorate the two enlarged capital letters at the beginning of this prayer.

Think about this!

Decorated letters are often used for prayers, poems and mottoes.
Scribes spent weeks and even years painting beautiful pictures to decorate the first capital letter on the page of a book.
Make a bookmark and decorate it with the initials of your name.

D ear

G od,

Who watches over all creatures,
Watch over me, at home and at school.

38 A speed writing test

Try writing each of these tongue-twisters as quickly as you can on separate sheets of paper. Can you keep your handwriting neat?

The quick brown fox jumps over the lazy dog.

Around the rugged rock, the ragged rascal ran.

39 It's an apostrophe!

Which of the **its** and **it's** in the following sentences should have an apostrophe and which should not? Write the corrected sentences on another sheet of paper.

> **Think about this!**
>
> If you can split **it's** into **it is** without destroying the sense of the sentence, it should have an apostrophe. If you can't, it shouldn't!

The cat was washing its whiskers.

The old oak tree had shed its leaves in the autumn gales.

Its a good thing I brought my umbrella.

When you think its going to be sunny, it often rains.

40

Write the words in the box in alphabetical order. Then practise reading and spelling them with your partner.

Think about this!

To help you remember these words, practise writing each one at least five times.
Remember to Look, Say, Cover, Write and Check!
Try not to lift your pencil off the paper until you have finished a whole word.
When you have finished, place your pencil on the line and try writing each word again with your eyes closed.

> below following different along both across
> also between inside high around above

Some words you should know

Write the words in the box in alphabetical order. Then practise reading and spelling them with your partner.

Think about this!

To help you remember these words, practise writing each one at least five times.
Remember to Look, Say, Cover, Write and Check!
Try not to lift your pencil off the paper until you have finished a whole word.
When you have finished, place your pencil on the line and try writing each word again with your eyes closed.

where other near together round outside
such place without through right under

_____

_____

_____

_____

_____

_____

_____

_____

_____

_____

Write the following unusual epitaphs found on gravestones.
You might use your research skills to find some more examples.

Stay, selfish man
And drop a tear.
Jane's little bird
Lies buried here.

Here lies what's left
Of Leslie Moore.
No Les,
No more.

Sir Vere-Burns RIP
Here lies a man who was
killed by lightning;
He died when his prospects
seemed to be brightening.
He might have cut a flash in
this world of trouble,
But the flash cut him and he
lies in the stubble.

43 Design a poster

These phrases are all used when people want to sell something.
Use them to help you write a newspaper advertisement selling an
imaginary item. Then design a poster advertising the item for sale.

Think about this!

When advertising items for sale, people often use print instead of joined writing to highlight important words and phrases. Sometimes they will enlarge, **highlight** or *italicise* words.

Each word costs money, so think where you might use a dash instead of a complete sentence to save space.

For Sale   one careful owner   still boxed
slightly shopsoiled   some attention needed
in perfect condition   free to a good home
can deliver   price reflects condition
good with children   would suit large family

_____

_____

_____

_____

_____

_____

_____

_____

Handwriting check 5:
Proverbs

Write each of the following proverbs in your best handwriting.

A fair exchange is no robbery.

_____

_____

_____

A bird in the hand is worth two in the bush.

_____

_____

_____

Don't count your chickens before they are hatched.

_____

_____

_____

Don't put all your eggs in one basket.

_____

_____

_____

45 Handwriting check 6:
"From a Railway Carriage"

Write this poem in your best handwriting.

Think about this!

Look carefully at all of the punctuation marks used in this poem. Why has each one been chosen? How do they help you to read the poem out loud?

Faster than fairies, faster than witches,
Bridges and houses, hedges and ditches;
And charging along like troops in a battle,
All through the meadows, the horses and cattle;
All of the sights of the hill and the plain
Fly as thick as driving rain;
And ever again, in the wink of an eye,
Painted stations whistle by.

Here is a child who clambers and scrambles,
All by himself and gathering brambles;
Here is a tramp who stands and gazes;
And there is the green for stringing the daisies!
Here is a cart run away in the road
Lumping along with man and load;
And here is a mill, and there is a river:
Each a glimpse and gone for ever!

Robert Louis Stevenson

Write this letter in your best handwriting, then use it to write your own letter to show your parents or carers how well you can write.

Think about this!

Everyone has someone special to thank for helping them learn to do things well. It might be your family, teachers or friends.
You could even design your own headed notepaper and envelopes to make your letter extra special.

Dear Mum and Dad,

As you can see, I have been learning joined handwriting. I still find some letters quite hard but I am very proud of how neat it is. I thought it would be a good idea to write you a letter to say thank you for all the things you do for me. Thank you for making sure I have delicious food to eat and a cosy warm bed to go to sleep in. Thank you for taking me out on trips and for buying me a computer so that I can surf the Internet. I like all my toys and games and most of all I like watching television.

Thank you for being my Mum and Dad.

Love from

Write this poem in your best handwriting. You might want
to learn it by heart.

Think about this!

This famous poem has a very strong rhythm.
John Masefield loved the sound of words and selected
them very carefully.
Several commas in a sentence help you to slow
down when you read it. Where there are fewer commas
you can speed up when you read.

Quinquereme of Nineveh from distant Ophir
Rowing home to haven in sunny Palestine,
With a cargo of ivory,
And apes and peacocks,
Sandalwood, cedarwood, and sweet white wine.

Stately Spanish galleon coming from the Isthmus,
Dipping through the Tropics by the palm-green
shores,
With a cargo of diamonds,
Emeralds, amethysts,
Topazes, and cinnamon and gold moidores.

Dirty British coaster with a salt-caked smoke
stack
Butting through the channel in the mad March
days,
With a cargo of Tyne coal,
Road-rail, pig-lead,
Firewood, iron-ware, and cheap tin trays.

John Masefield